Busy Days Away
Activity book with stickers

D1460889

EGMONT

First published in Great Britain in 2014 by Egmont UK Limited,
The Yellow Building, 1 Nicholas Road, London W11 4AN

Thomas the Tank Engine & Friends™

CREATED BY BRITT ALLCROFT

Based on the Railway Series by the Reverend W Awdry
© 2014 Gullane (Thomas) LLC. A HIT Entertainment company.
Thomas the Tank Engine & Friends and Thomas & Friends are trademarks of Gullane (Thomas) Limited.
Thomas the Tank Engine & Friends and Design is Reg. U.S. Pat. & Tm. Off.

ISBN 978 1 4052 7308 4
57733/1

Printed in Italy

HiT entertainment

Well Done!

SODOR

Well Done!

Well Done!

Can you find all of these in the big picture?

Toby

Gordon

Henry

Edward

Emily

Blue car

James

Charlie

Percy

Bertie

At Tidmouth Sheds

Welcome to the Engine Sheds
where Thomas and his friends are
ready to be Really Useful Engines.
But some of his friends are missing.

Can you add stickers of Henry, Thomas and Emily to the scene?

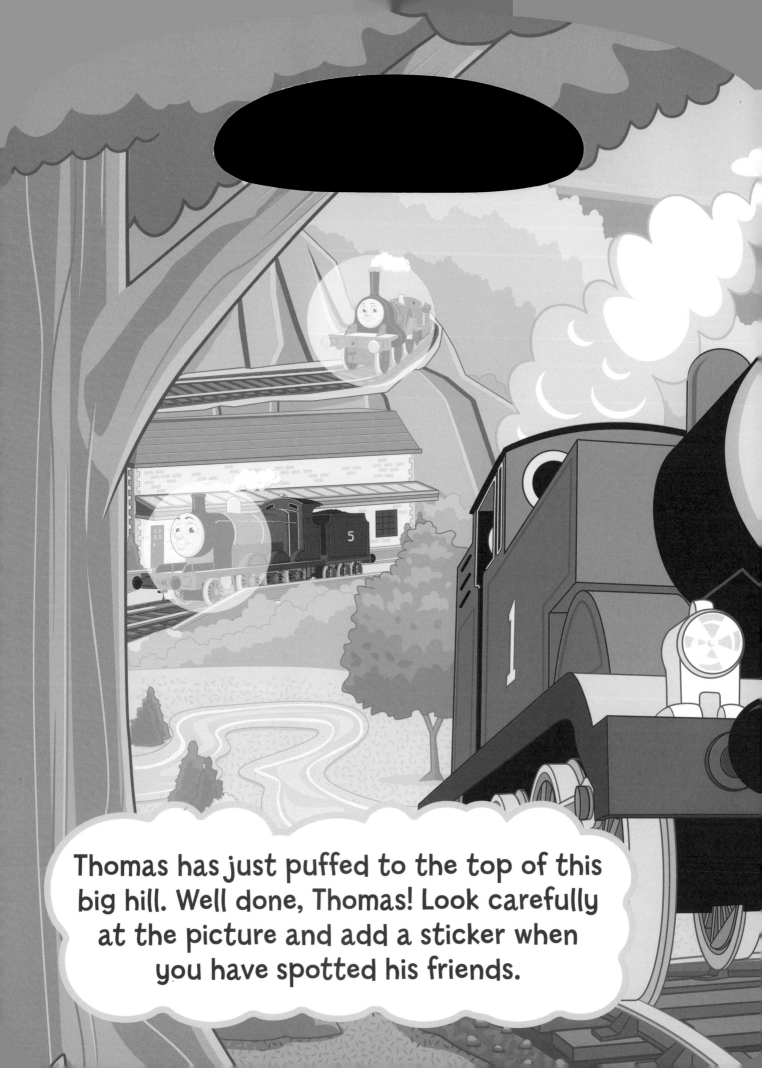

Thomas has just puffed to the top of this big hill. Well done, Thomas! Look carefully at the picture and add a sticker when you have spotted his friends.

Well Done, Thomas!

Can you spot
all of these
green things?
- Percy
- Cranky
- bridge
- lamp post

Get Set, Go!

Thomas and Bertie love to race.
Say, "Peep! Peep! Beep! Beep!"
as they meet at the bridge.

START

First use your finger to show Thomas the way along the track. Then do the same with Bertie along the road. Who would you like to win the race?

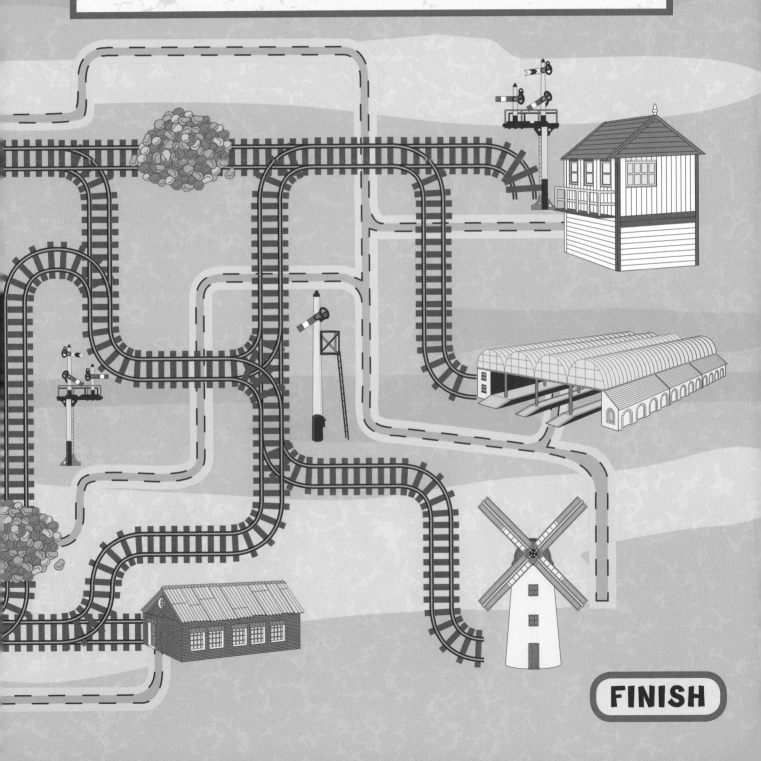

FINISH

Let's Count

Trace your finger over the number **1**.
Then try with a crayon.

Sticker

Put a number 1
sticker here!

One
Thomas

Can you write the number **2**?

Sticker

Put a number **2** sticker here!

Two coaches

Let's Count

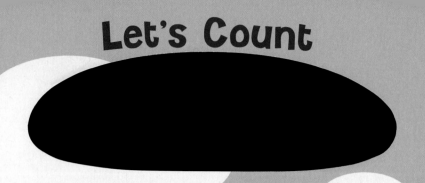

Trace your finger over the number **3**.
Then try with a crayon.

3

Sticker

Put a number 3
sticker here!

Three
Troublesome
Trucks

Can you write the number **4**?

Sticker

Put a number **4** sticker here!

Four friends

Let's Count

Trace your finger over the number **5**.
Then try with a crayon.

5

Sticker

Put a number 5
sticker here!

Five
passengers

Can you write the number **6**?

Sticker

Put a number **6** sticker here!

Six engine bays

Let's Count

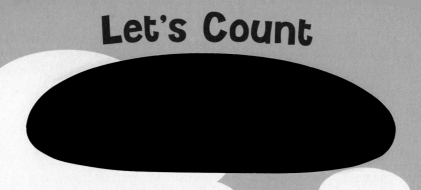

Trace your finger over the number **7**.
Then try with a crayon.

7

Sticker

Put a number **7** sticker here!

Seven suitcases

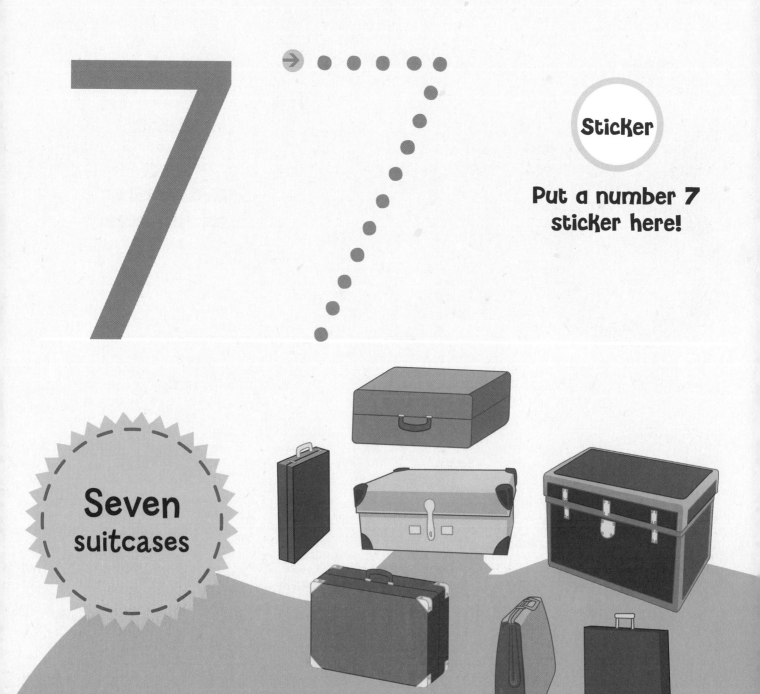

Can you write the number **8**?

8

Sticker

Put a number 8
sticker here!

Eight
flags

Let's Count

Trace your finger over the number **9**.
Then try with a crayon.

Sticker

Put a number **9**
sticker here!

Nine
signals

Can you write the number **10**?

10

Ten seagulls

Sticker

Put a number **10** sticker here!

Let's Count

Now try counting all the way from **1** to **10** again.

Maithwaite

1 2 3 4 5

1 2 3 4 5

1 2 3 4 5

Let's Count

There are lots of things to count in this picture.
How many engines are there?
How many clouds? How many guards?

All About Blue

Thomas
is blue.

Colour in this picture using a bright blue crayon.

Kevin is yellow.

Join the dots to finish Kevin's heavy crate and then colour in this picture of Kevin using a yellow crayon.

All About Black

Hiro is
black.

Using a black crayon, colour in this picture of
The Fat Controller talking to Hiro.

All About Purple

Rosie is
purple.

Colour in this pretty picture using a purple crayon.

All About Green

Percy is green.

Follow the dots to finish Percy's puff of steam and then colour in this picture using a green crayon.

All About Red

James
is red.

Using a red crayon, colour in this picture of
James with his friend Bertie.

Round and Round

Thomas' wheels are circles!
Have a go at drawing your own circle.

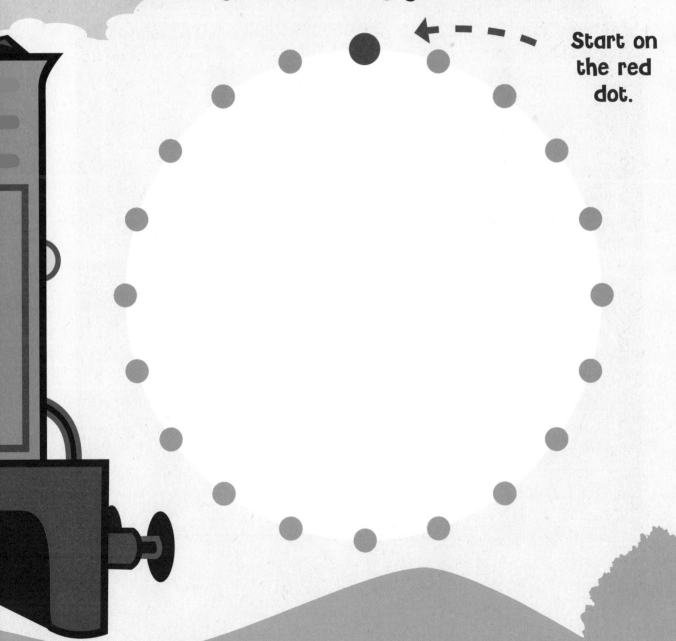

Start on the red dot.

Look around you.
Can you see anything that is a circle?

Super Squares

Toby's face is a square!

Now draw a square with beautiful straight lines.

Look around you.
Can you see anything that is a square?

Terrific Triangles

The station roofs
are triangles!

Can you draw a triangle?
It has three pointy corners.

Look around you.
Can you see anything that is a triangle?

Maithwaite

Bertie's face is a rectangle!
You'll need straight lines to draw a rectangle.

Look around you.
Can you see anything that is a rectangle?

Shining Stars

Colour in these stars with your brightest yellow crayon.

How many stars are in the sky?

Super Shapes

Now try drawing all the
shapes you have learnt.

You can colour the
shapes in too.

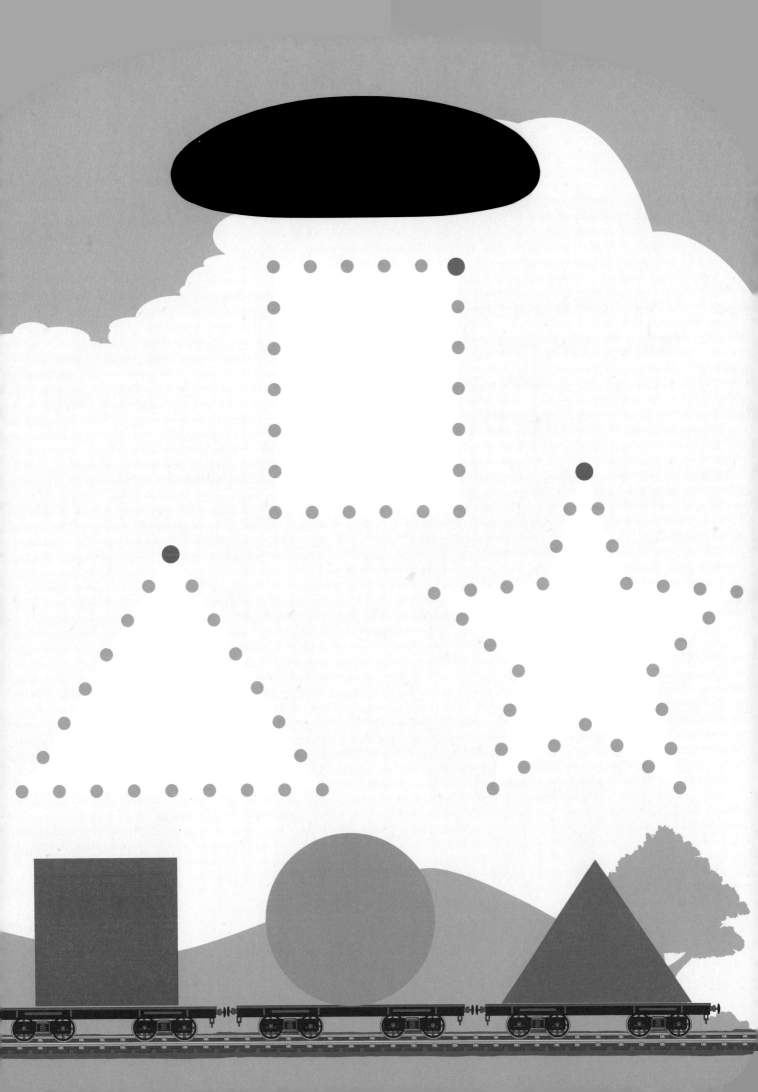

Who's Who?

Thomas

Kevin

Rosie

James

Bertie

Now that you have met lots of different vehicles and coloured them in, see if you can match them to their shadows.

A Perfect Match

All the engines on The Fat Controller's railway work together as a team but some like to work in special pairs.

Can you match these engines and coaches into their pairs?

Spot the Difference

In one of these pictures Thomas is looking happy and in the other he is looking surprised. Point to happy Thomas.

There are also four other differences in the second picture. Give yourself a sticker when you have found them all.

Sticker

Train Spotting

★ 1

These two pictures of Percy, Thomas and James
look the same but there are five differences.
Can you find them all?

2

When you've found all five
give yourself a sticker.

Sticker

Let's Colour

Sticker

This small engine is Charlie. When you are
out and about see if you can spot an engine.
Add a sticker when you have seen one.

Use the small pictures to help you colour in your own.

Sticker

The Fat Controller has a very smart, blue car.
Add a sticker when you spot a car outside.

Let's Colour

CRANKY

Use the small pictures to help you colour in your own.

Cranky is a crane. He is the tallest vehicle on the Island of Sodor. Have you ever seen a crane?

Sticker

Sticker

Jack is a Really Useful red digger.
Add a sticker when you spot a digger outside.

Let's Colour

Use the small pictures to help you colour in your own.

Sticker

Harold the Helicopter is a Really Useful machine. He can land on water as well as land. Have you ever seen a helicopter?

Flynn the Fire Engine is always ready to race to the rescue. Add a sticker when you spot a fire engine outside.

Sticker

Let's Colour

Use the small pictures to help you colour in your own.

Captain is a wooden rescue boat.
He braves the biggest storms.
If you see a boat add a sticker here.

Sticker

Sticker

Bertie the Bus takes passengers all over the Island of Sodor. He always tries to be on time. Add a sticker when you spot a bus outside.

Goat

Thomas loves to look out for animals as he chuffs by. Next time you're on a journey see if you can spot these animals.

Draw lots of tasty grass and flowers for this goat to eat.

Cow

Colour in this cow.

On the Farm

Pig

Colour in the pig with a pink crayon.

Duck

Join up the dots to give this duck a friend.

On the Farm

Hen

Can you draw some baby chicks
next to the mother hen?

Dog

Can you draw some toys for
this dog to play with?

Can you find all of these in the big picture?

James

workman

Kevin

lamp

Percy

cable reel

Victor

oil drum

Thomas

The Fat Controller

Goodnight, Thomas

FINISH

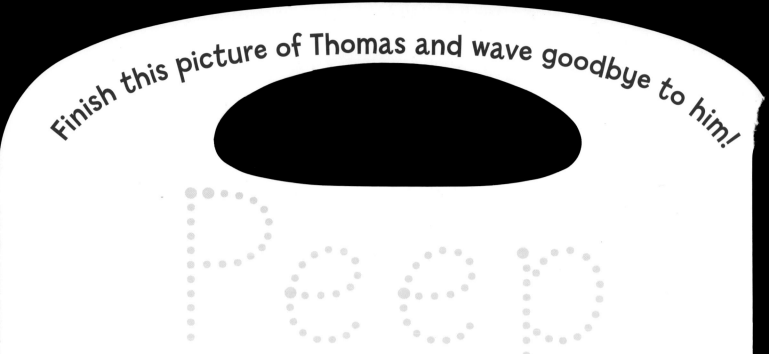

Peep